T0061466

James
MacMillan

St Luke Passion
The Passion of Our Lord Jesus Christ
according to Luke

for chorus, children's choir,
organ & chamber orchestra

Christus score
(children's choir)

Boosey & Hawkes Music Publishers Ltd
www.boosey.com

DISTRIBUTED BY HAL LEONARD

8 88680 09496 6
48023593

St Luke Passion

Contents

Co-commissioned by Stichting Omroep Muziek / NTR ZaterdagMatinee Amsterdam with assistance from the Royal Concertgebouw; Duke University; the City of Birmingham Symphony Orchestra, to mark the 40th anniversary of the CBSO Chorus; Soli Deo Gloria, Inc (USA) and Britten Sinfonia, with generous support from donors to its Musically Gifted campaign.

Performance note: Grace notes always on the beat

The commission has been made possible by a financial contribution from the Composition Commission Fund of The Royal Concertgebouw. The Composition Commission Fund is set up by a private donor with the intention of stimulating the development of new music and reaching a larger audience. The fund is managed by Het Concertgebouw Fonds.

The commission has also been made possible through a collaboration between members of Duke Divinity School and the Divinity School of the University of Cambridge, overseen by Duke Initiatives in Theology and the Arts. The collaboration has been funded by Duke Divinity School, The Mary Duke Biddle Foundation and Duke University Council for the Arts.

Published by Boosey & Hawkes Music Publishers Ltd
Aldwych House
71–91 Aldwych
London
WC2B 4HN

www.boosey.com

AN IMAGEM COMPANY

© Copyright 2013 by Boosey & Hawkes Music Publishers Ltd
Lyrics adapted from The Catholic Edition of the Revised Standard Version of the Bible, copyright 1965, 1966 by the Division of Christian Education of the National Council of the Churches of Christ in the United States of America. Used by permission. All rights reserved.

ISMN 979-0-060-12979-7
ISBN 978-1-78454-070-8

First impression 2015

Printed by Halstan:
Halstan UK, 2–10 Plantation Road, Amersham, Bucks, HP6 6HJ. United Kingdom
Halstan DE, Weißliliengasse 4, 55116 Mainz. Germany

Piano reduction by Christopher Brown
Music origination by The Note Factory

IMPORTANT NOTICE: The unauthorised copying of the whole or any part of this publication is illegal

to Jeremy Begbie

ST LUKE PASSION

**Christus
(children's choir)**

JAMES MACMILLAN
(b 1959)

Prelude

TACET

Chapter 22

TACET until

8 **a tempo subito (Allegro** ♩ = *c* 132 **)**

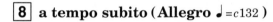

18 Tenor

he went a - way and con - ferred with the chief priests and

22

cap - tains how _____ he might be - tray him to them. And they were

25

glad, and en-gaged to give him mo - ney. So he a - greed, and sought an

29

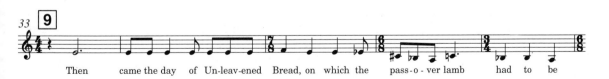

op - por - tu - ni - ty to be - tray him to them in the ab-sence of the mul - ti - tude.

33 **9**

Then came the day of Un-leav-ened Bread, on which the pass-o - ver lamb had to be

© Copyright 2013 by Boosey & Hawkes Music Publishers Ltd
Lyrics adapted from The Catholic Edition of the Revised Standard Version of the Bible,
copyright 1965, 1966 by the Division of Christian Education of the National Council of the
Churches of Christ in the United States of America. Used by permission. All rights reserved.

19423

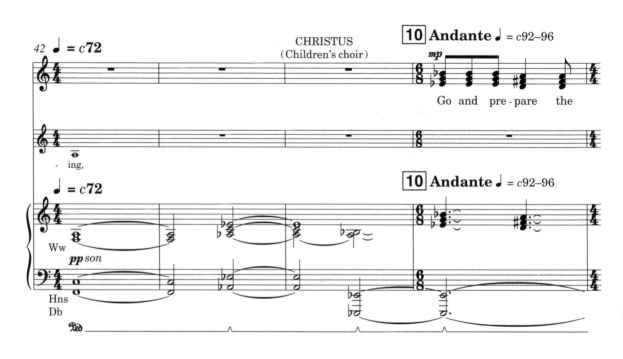

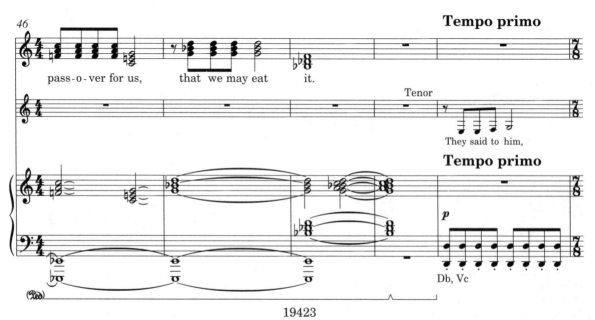

fol-low him in-to the house which he en-ters, and tell the house-hold-er, — "The

Teach-er says to you, Where is the guest room, where I am to eat the pass-o-ver

— with my dis-ci-ples?" And he will show you a large room fur-nished;

there make read-y.

Fl, Obs

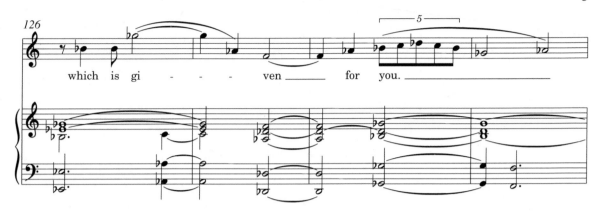

which is gi - - - ven _____ for you. _____

Do this _____ in re - mem - - - -

- - brance of _____ me. _____

Poco più mosso

Soprano

And _____ like - wise the

Poco più mosso

Ww

12

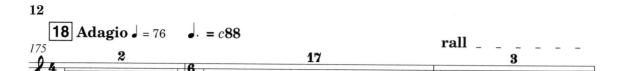

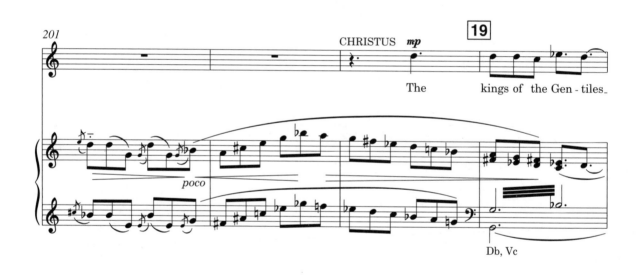

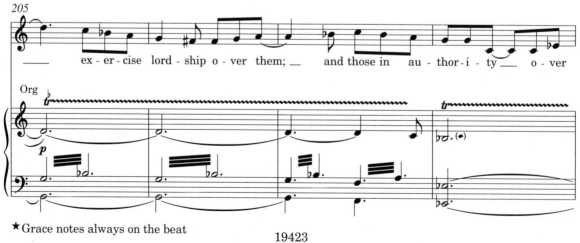

★Grace notes always on the beat

that he ___ might sift you ___ like ___ wheat, _____

but I have prayed for you that your faith ___ may

not ___ fail, _____ that your faith ___ may not fail;

and when you have turned a - gain; streng - - then your

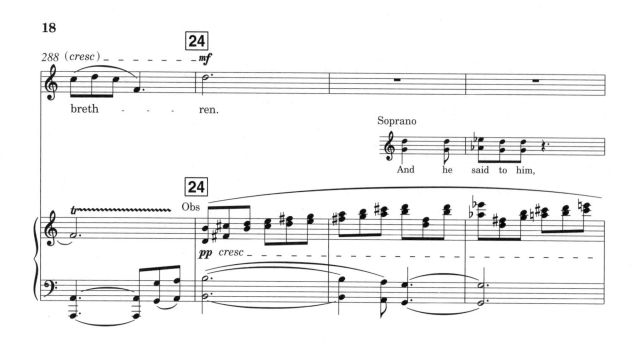

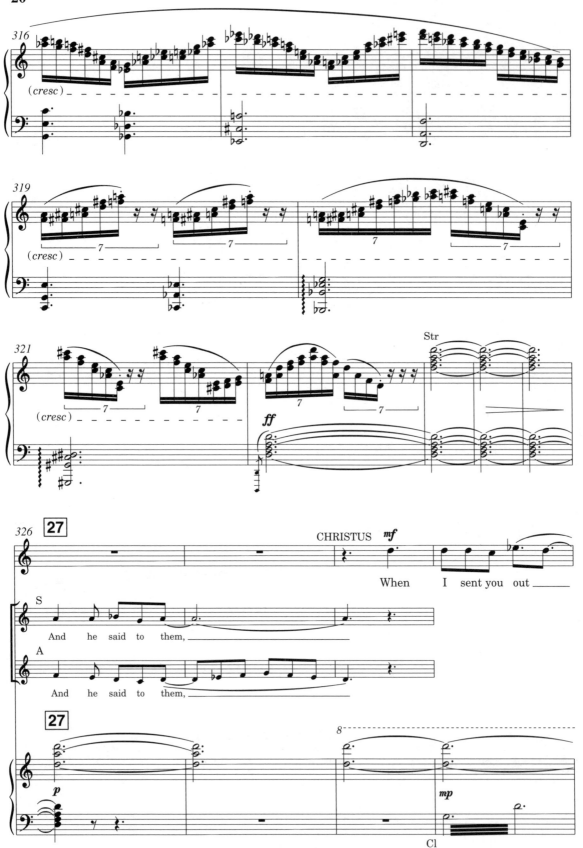

28 CHRISTUS

★ Grace notes always on the beat

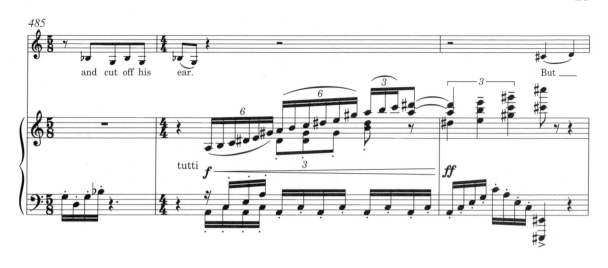

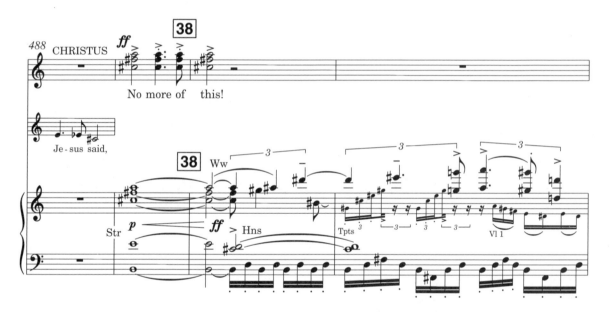

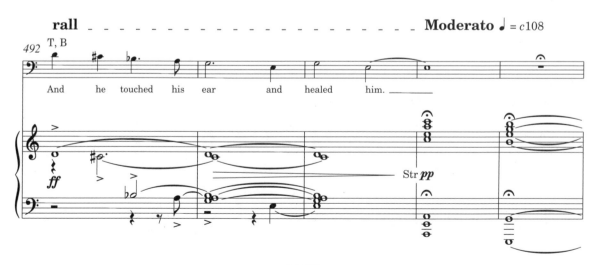

497 **39** Bass

Then Je - sus said to the chief priests and cap - tains of the

501

rall _ _ _ _ _ _

tem - - ple and el - ders, who had come out a -

504 (rall) _ _ _ _ _ **Meno mosso**

CHRISTUS

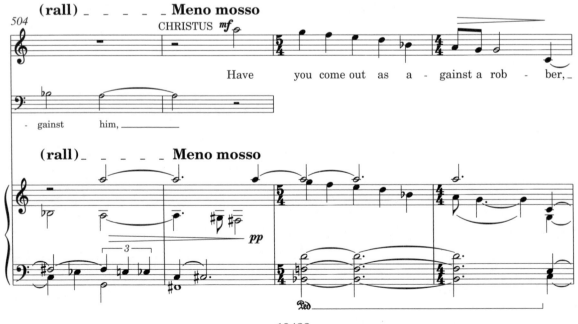

Have you come out as a - gainst a rob - ber, _

- gainst him, _

(rall) _ _ _ _ _ **Meno mosso**

with swords and clubs? — When I was with you day af-ter day in the

tem - ple, you did not lay hands — on me. But this is your

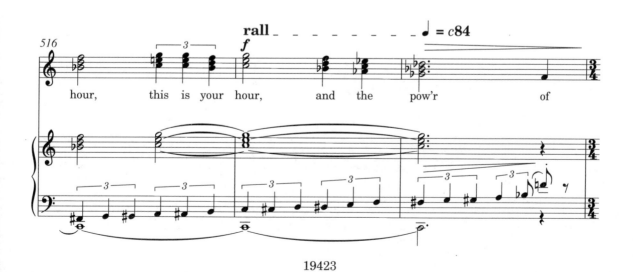

hour, this is your hour, and the pow'r of

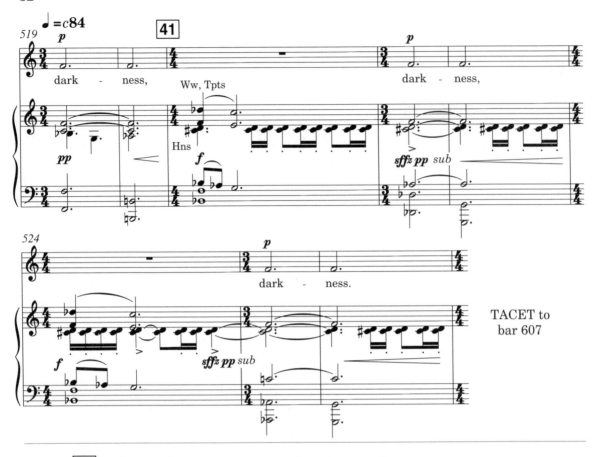

Chapter 23

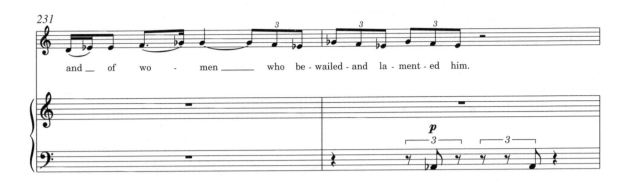

and — of wo - men ——— who be - wailed - and la - ment - ed him.

rall _ _ _ _ _ _ _ _ _ _ _

But Je - - sus turn - ing to them ——————— said, ——

71 **Larghetto** ♩ = c63

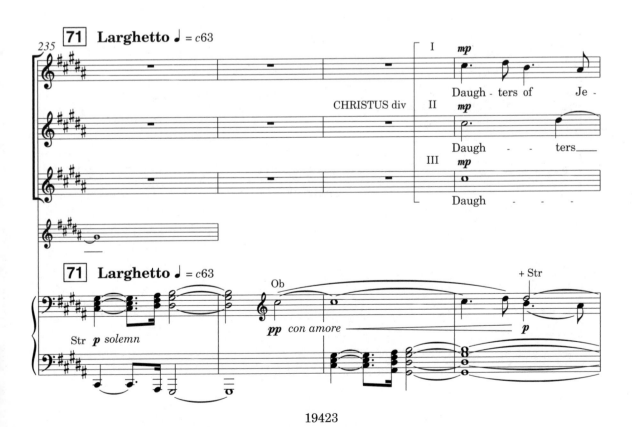

I *mp*

Daugh - ters of Je -

CHRISTUS div II *mp*

Daugh - - ters—

III *mp*

Daugh - - -

71 **Larghetto** ♩ = c63

Ob + Str

Str *p solemn*

pp con amore ——————— *p*

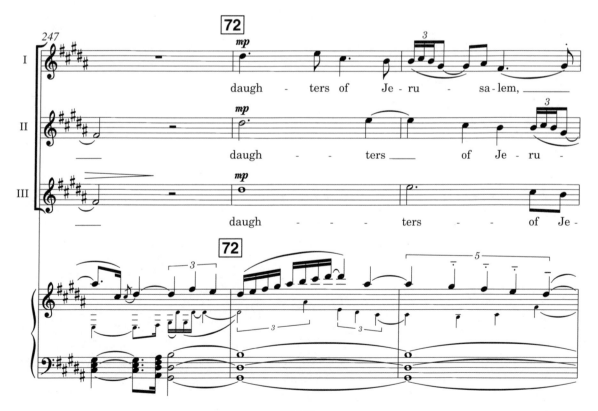

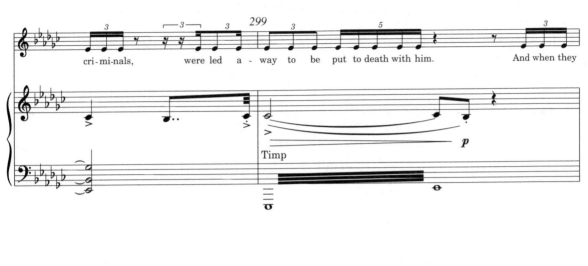

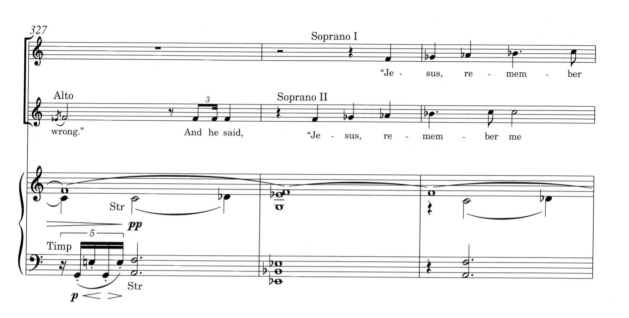

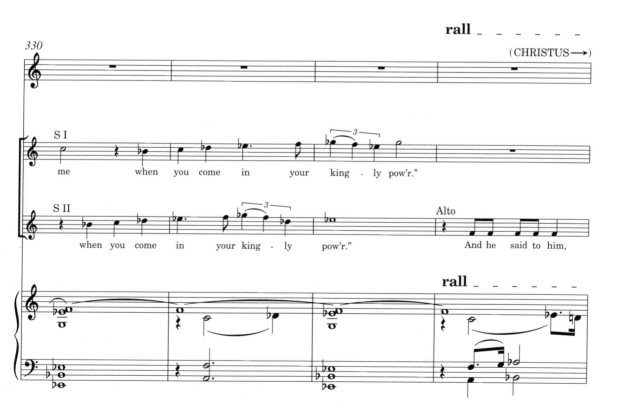

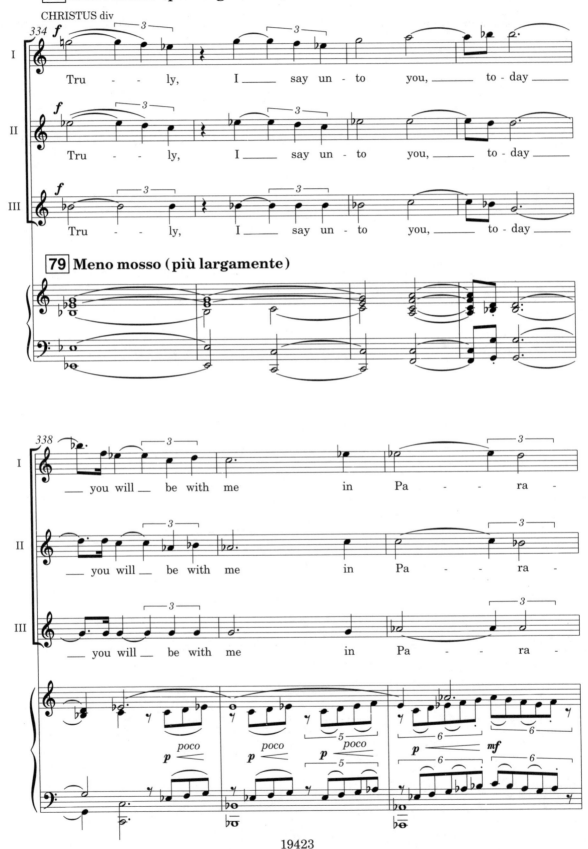

Postlude

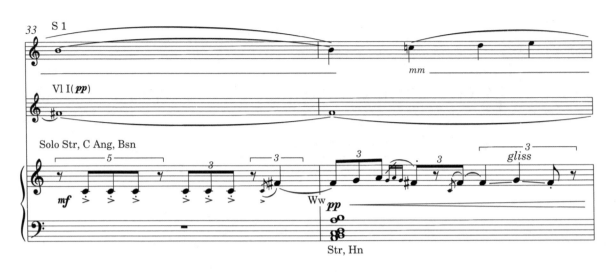

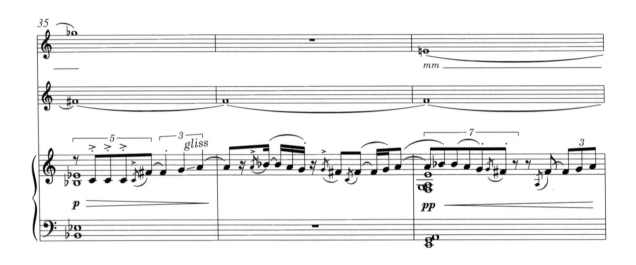

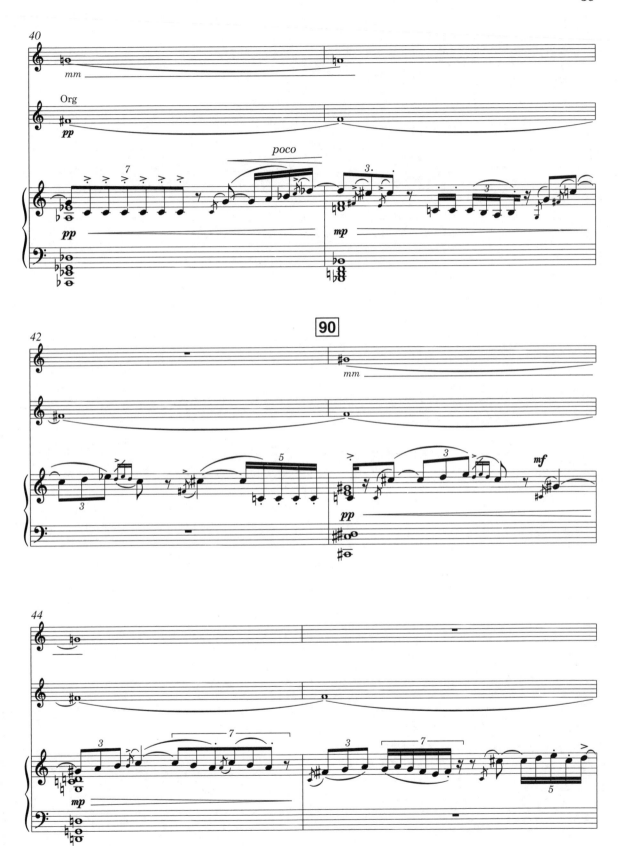

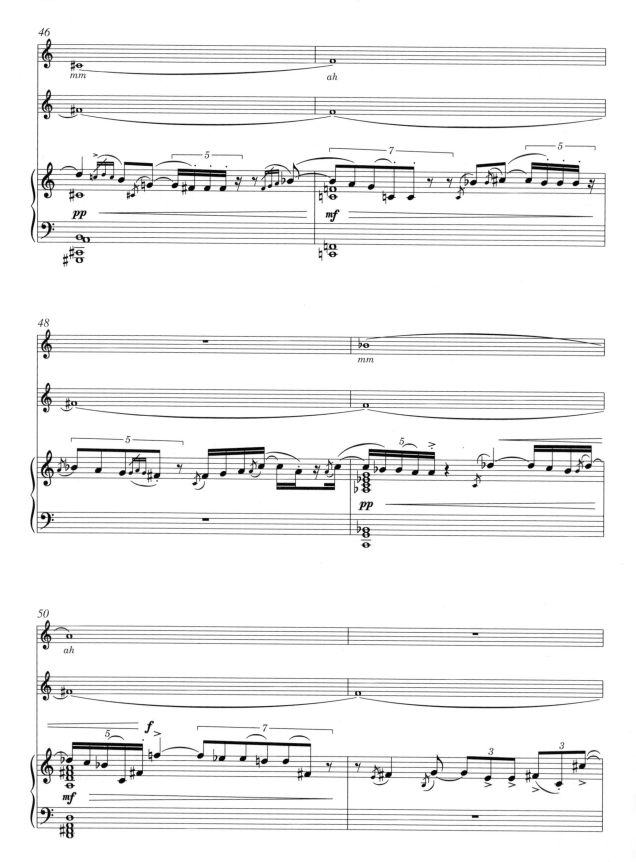

ISBN 978-1-78454-070-8

ISMN 979-0-060-12979-7